LARGE PRINT CROSSWORDS™

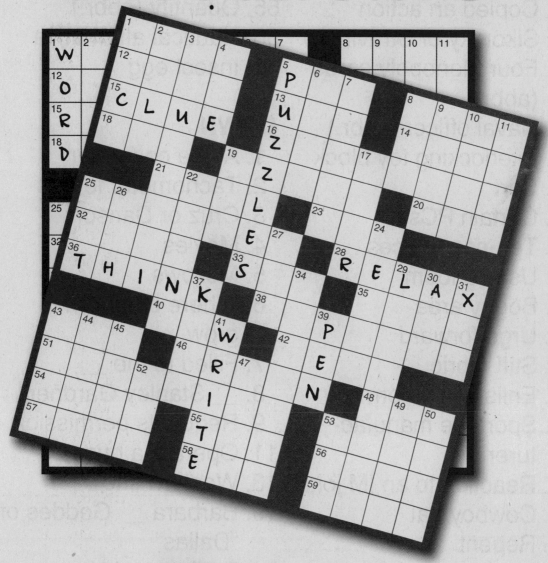

D1096055

KAPPA Books

Visit us at www.kappabooks.com

Crossword 1

ACROSS

1. Bejeweled "A-Team" star (2 wds.)
4. Wonderful, slangily
7. Fergie's firstborn
10. Copied an action
12. Sikorsky or Stravinsky
14. Four Monopoly cards (abbr.)
15. Naval officer (abbr.)
16. Interlocking toy block
17. Sort
18. Certain PCs
20. Ten-cent pieces
22. Uses a loom
25. Boggy area
26. Urge forward
27. Stiff fabric
31. Enlistees, informally
32. Sportage manufacturer
33. Reaction to an IM joke
34. Cowboy hat
37. Repent
39. Exclamations of surprise
40. Parmesan or ricotta
41. Lawn trimmer
44. Soothe
45. Cariou of "Blue Bloods"
46. Eternally
48. Spat
52. Mariner's milieu
53. Cager Chamberlain
54. Israeli dance
55. Quantity (abbr.)
56. Nautical affirmative
57. Insect egg

DOWN

1. Apple computer
2. Tachometer letters
3. Cruz or Danson
4. Movies
5. Mellows
6. Where cranberries grow
7. Filled to the __
8. __ Stanley Gardner
9. Requests permission
11. Operate a bus
13. Western show
19. Barbara __ Geddes of "Dallas"
21. Business abbr.
22. Barristers' wear
23. Give off
24. Church wing

25. Friar's title
27. Storage box
28. __ vera
29. Adams and Rickles
30. Robert __ (2 wds.)
32. Ring results (abbr.)
35. Boot front
36. Mole's kin
37. Cries of delight

38. Incisors
40. Menu
41. "Frozen" princess
42. Think
43. Tiny fly
44. Slippery
47. Itinerary word
49. Charged atom
50. Part of TGIF (abbr.)
51. "__ chance!"

Crossword 2

ACROSS

1. Lawyers' org.
4. BB's, e.g.
8. Haley, to Luke Dunphy
11. Modern diagnostic tool (abbr.)
12. Grizzly __
13. 1950s crooner Paul
14. Fish feature
15. __ B'rith
16. Female Egyptian ruler, for short
17. Procedure
19. "Scram!"
21. "__ a Small World"
22. Ablaze
25. Seuss's were green
28. Mammal's three
29. Stir
31. Fawn's parent
32. 2:1, e.g.
34. Bowler's target
35. Mom's boy
36. __ bind (2 wds.)
37. Kitchen or major ender
38. Dashboard button
40. Lgs.' opposites (abbr.)
42. Course (abbr.)

43. Or's partner
47. Food for Fido
50. Path
52. Mrs., to Pierre
53. Gloom and __
54. Writer Bombeck
55. Canola __
56. Miss Piggy's word for "me"
57. Time divisions
58. Pig's place

DOWN

1. Type of radio (hyph.)
2. Cocktail party cheese
3. Slangy negative
4. Chief monk
5. Repairs
6. Goat's bleat
7. Paper-folding craft
8. Late night weekend comedy show (abbr.)
9. Alibi __
10. __ Paulo
13. Play opener (2 wds.)
18. That man's
20. That being the case (2 wds.)
23. Very attentive
24. Brush up a manuscript
25. McMahon and McBain
26. __ as gold

27. Heredity factor
28. Airline schedule abbr.
30. Dollar bill
32. Rampage
33. Enraged
37. Guess at a price (abbr.)
39. "Pennies __ Heaven"
40. Sordid
41. Golden-touch king
44. Modern physicians' gps.
45. Send forth
46. Bank (on)
47. Byrd's rank (abbr.)
48. Brit's bathroom
49. Luau dish
51. "... a man __ mouse?" (2 wds.)

Crossword 3

ACROSS

1. Abbr. on a timetable
4. San Francisco's __ Hill
7. Lackland, for one (abbr.)
10. Businessman's neckwear
11. Bug
13. Goose formation
14. Abbr. on a speeding ticket
15. Don't disturb (2 wds.)
16. Suffix for suburban or meteor
17. "Old MacDonald" refrain letters
19. Prying tool
21. Enjoy oneself (3 wds.)
25. Grant of "Notorious"
26. Waitress on "Alice"
27. "__ Love Again" (2 wds.)
31. Tax agcy.
32. Road sealant
33. City railways
34. Suppose
36. Ambulance worker (abbr.)
37. Cow's offspring
38. Menaces
41. __ Lama
44. Blushing
45. Midafternoon, on a clock
46. Deputized band
50. Computer exit (abbr.)
53. Lemon drink
54. Sleeper's noise
55. Purge
56. "__ Misérables"
57. Kimono sash
58. Fathers of Jrs.

DOWN

1. Modern bank teller (abbr.)
2. Shred
3. Practice for a play
4. Compass pt.
5. Canadian prov.
6. Sassy hairdo
7. Tel __
8. Fancy party
9. Malt beverage
11. Sunburn-soothing plant
12. Shriek
18. __ League college
20. Hebrew priest
21. Aesop's bad example
22. Following

23. Condemn
24. Major artery
25. El ___
28. Wanders about
29. Maladies
30. Bounced check inits.
35. NYC transit gp.
37. Mediocre mark
39. Hula hoop twirlers
40. Squirrel's haven

41. Timepiece face
42. Campaign helper
43. Deceives
47. "Sail ___ Ship of State!" (2 wds.)
48. Cry loudly
49. ___ Lanka
51. Churchill's title
52. Bank offerings (abbr.)

Crossword 4

ACROSS

1. Swedish rock group
5. Had a nibble
8. Squeak by
11. __ year
12. Actor Bogarde
14. Author Anaïs __
15. Coagulates
16. Chef Paula __
17. Children's game
18. Blossom
20. "__ Believer" (2 wds.)
22. Officeholders
23. Yard enclosure
26. Kilt pattern
29. Frozen waffle brand
30. Sheep's covering
31. "Heidi" mountains
32. Graceland name
34. Certain Scandinavians
36. Choose for office
37. Little pooch, for short
38. Church lecture (abbr.)
39. Engraved on glass
43. Inits. for Charlemagne
45. Sci. course
47. Jacob's brother
49. Alias initials
50. __ log
51. Rainy times (abbr.)
52. Attained
53. Size between sm. and lg.
54. Applies henna

DOWN

1. High-school course (abbr.)
2. Complaint
3. Palace dance
4. Lhasa __ (Tibetan terrier)
5. Number to be totaled
6. Stadium sections
7. Sooner than, poetically
8. Become snarled
9. Korean auto name
10. London's locale (abbr.)
13. Cutting tool
19. Popular Nintendo product
21. Actress Mullally

24. __ and robbers
25. Curvy letter
26. Gallup survey
27. Small sofa (2 wds.)
28. "Still __" (2014 film)
30. __ small hours
33. Lost animal
34. Covered with spots
35. Gremlin co.
37. Dr. Norman Vincent __
40. Cabbage unit
41. See at a distance
42. Challenge
43. Witch
44. Movie monogram
46. Old Testament bk.
48. American ship abbr.

Crossword 5

ACROSS

1. Vigoda et al.
5. Science study (abbr.)
8. Middle (abbr.)
11. "Cool!"
12. Pt. of speech
13. Univ. housing
14. Scarlett's estate
15. Half a fly
16. To __ (unanimous, 2 wds.)
17. Mischievous
19. Inclined way
21. Thumbs-down votes
22. Dreary
24. Having weapons
27. Puppy's bite
28. Umbrella support
30. Nothing special
31. Zeus, e.g.
32. Aspiring band's CD
33. Digital watch display (abbr.)
34. Historical period
35. In need of tidying
36. Scoundrel
38. Adversary
39. Frosts a cake
40. Forces back
44. Laurie or Hefner
46. Chinese leader
48. Killed, as a dragon
49. Tennis great Arthur
50. Actress __ B. Davis
51. Director Kazan
52. Head topper
53. Banned insecticide (abbr.)
54. Society (abbr.)

DOWN

1. One opposed
2. Timber piece
3. Wyatt __
4. Wood finisher
5. Soaking spots
6. Passports, e.g., for short
7. Make a higher auction offer
8. Likens
9. Refrain word
10. Presidential monogram
13. Baronet's wife
18. Turf
20. High mountain
23. Novak et al.

24. ___-CIO (labor group)
25. Magazine stand
26. Cinderella's "curfew"
27. Pierre's refusal
29. Cub scout, for example
31. Loses it (2 wds.)
32. ___ diver (hyph.)
34. Eden lady
35. Bossy Stooge

37. Muscle soreness
38. Facade
41. Added additions
42. Flower garlands
43. Graceful creature
44. Cry of triumph
45. Chant at the Olympics
47. "Mutt ___ Jeff"

Crossword 6

ACROSS

1. Pot cover
4. Prohibits
8. Closest buddy, to a texter
11. "In your dreams!" (2 wds.)
13. Over
14. Eng. course
15. __ Rabbit
16. Roman 156
17. Insert
18. "Yuck!"
20. Reverberate
22. Kind of ranch
24. Lazily
26. Rose Bowl locale
28. Coming out gals
32. Shoshonean
33. Make disappear
35. Pasture
36. "The World According to __"
38. Breathing in
40. General Robert __ (2 wds.)
42. Average grades
43. __-mutton (hyph.)
45. F followers
46. Race the motor
47. Art __ (decorative art)
50. Hunter's prey
54. Lamb's mother
55. Whipped-cream serving
56. Wind instrument
57. ID digits
58. Heart tests (abbr.)
59. Psychedelic drug (abbr.)

DOWN

1. Chemist's workshop
2. Neighbor of Syria (abbr.)
3. The __ is cast
4. Opposite of front
5. Part of NATO (abbr.)
6. Fall mo.
7. Hawker's come-on
8. In need of pepping up
9. Rover's friend
10. Florist letters
12. Mexican painter Kahlo
19. Give up
21. Dancer Charisse
22. Information bits
23. Wielder
24. Idiotic
25. Dot's companion
26. __ nose

27. Great Lakes port
29. Author Wiesel
30. Affleck and Vereen
31. Sink down
34. Apiece
37. Cribbage scorer
39. "GWTW" star
41. Fraternal organization's meeting place

43. Ayres and Wallace
44. Equal
45. Sailors
46. Home (abbr.)
48. Brotherhood brother
49. Gear tooth
51. Yahoo! alternative (abbr.)
52. "___ Doubtfire"
53. Finale

Crossword 7

ACROSS

1. Santa's busy mo.
4. Destroy, slangily
9. Cpl.'s boss
12. A Gershwin
13. Hair salon action
14. Intelligence org.
15. House wing
16. Stranger
17. One, in Lima
18. Synagogues
20. Columbus Day mo.
22. Gore et al.
23. Punched hard
26. Excludes
28. Free from guilt
29. Monetary liability
30. __ Tac (mint)
31. Furry swimmer
32. Washington peak
34. Prescriptions, informally
35. Playwright O'Neill
36. Hold session
37. Doghouse sound
38. Official reprimand
42. Tycoon Onassis
44. Word after work or moral
46. Fashionable, to Twiggy
47. Like Capp's Abner
48. Passing fashion
49. Boar
50. Morning hours (abbr.)
51. Fork prongs
52. Deceitful

DOWN

1. Try to reduce
2. __ Stanley Gardner
3. Peaceable
4. Mythical bridge denizens
5. Motors
6. No ifs, __, or buts
7. Compass pt.
8. Hayden Panettiere's TV series
9. Scurried
10. Cotton machine
11. Truth, in China
19. Business associate
21. Storage places
23. London TV network
24. Gabor et al.
25. Dolores __ Rio
26. Gentleman caller
27. Columnist Van Buren

et al.

28. Basketball filler
29. Rap's "Dr."
30. Baseball stand for tykes
33. Contaminate with germs
34. Chops fine

36. Take by force
38. Detective Charlie
39. Diamond figures, for short
40. Trouble the waters
41. Snappish
42. Pie __ mode (2 wds.)
43. Border
45. Cycle starter

Crossword 8

ACROSS

1. Trio before E
4. Monk's wear
8. Served perfectly
12. Great wrath
13. Diva's solo
14. Opening
15. Court divider
16. Number one
17. Peak
18. Davis of "Stuart Little"
20. Modern office fixtures (abbr.)
22. Boxing bout enders (abbr.)
23. Dancer Sally
25. Sword handle
27. ___ in arms
30. Drops of sweat
33. Crowning glory
34. Cul-de-___
36. Verdi opera
37. Otherwise (2 wds.)
39. Grabbed hold of the other guy, in football
41. Piercing tools
43. Cry softly
44. Siamese ___

46. ___ Guevara
48. Axiom
51. Got off
53. March date
55. Hold up
56. Unkempt person
57. Library charge
58. Keyboard button
59. Sermon subject
60. Mrs. Dick Tracy
61. Football units (abbr.)

DOWN

1. Crooner Crosby
2. Canadian Native American
3. Resoluteness
4. Bathhouse tent
5. Mine extract
6. Small amount
7. Gate closer
8. Exclamation of triumph
9. Certain social gathering (2 wds.)
10. Popular Muppet
11. They're worse than cees
19. Thin
21. Bro or sis
24. Cavity filler's deg.
26. Dripped water

27. Frat letter
28. Fellow lacking grace
29. Enjoy dinner
31. He took the reins from HST
32. Depressed
35. Crow's cry
38. Doting attention (abbr.)

40. Ends
42. Change position
44. TV panelist Peggy
45. "___ Know" (2 wds.)
47. Falco or Adams
49. Motivate
50. Subsides
52. Kitchen meas.
54. O'Toole's rank (abbr.)

Crossword 9

ACROSS

1. Its mama's a mare
5. Rope material
9. Charlotte's project
12. One-time New York nightclub, for short
13. Jai __
14. Bread type
15. Hershey's output (2 wds.)
18. Daredevil Knievel
19. Cod and Hope
20. True or __
23. Flower plot
24. "__ live and breathe!" (2 wds.)
25. Cagers' gp.
28. Strip of contention
32. Lingerie or menswear, e.g. (abbr.)
34. FBI worker (abbr.)
35. Mimi, Nicole, and Katie to Tom Cruise
36. Effortless
37. Anjou cousin
39. Historian's division
40. "Leaving __ Vegas"
42. Stocking material
44. Ski resort

47. Train hopper
49. Electrical problems (2 wds.)
54. Make edging
55. Vast periods of time
56. "__ as good a time as any"
57. Some ER cases
58. Blockhead
59. Pesky insect

DOWN

1. TV regulators (abbr.)
2. Delighted cry
3. Military address abbr.
4. Shoestrings
5. Hardy
6. Mideast airline (2 wds.)
7. Gym cushion
8. Portion
9. Sandwich's cousin
10. Jane of an 1847 novel
11. First lady after Eleanor
16. Cookie cooker
17. Boy Scout distinction
20. Lose brightness
21. Enjoying a cruise
22. "Read my __..."
23. Sluggers' needs
26. Hansoms
27. Way back when

29. Figure skater's jump
30. Nothing
31. "..._ elephant's eye" (2 wds.)
33. Mary __ Moore
38. Cable choice (abbr.)
41. Put a chip in the kitty
43. "__ at Heart"
44. Concerning (2 wds.)

45. Roe source
46. Cookware
47. Female deer
48. Words of approximation (2 wds.)
50. Pigeon's sound
51. Charged particle
52. Inits. once seen at airports
53. Speedy jet's letters

Crossword 10

ACROSS

1. AWOL pursuers
4. Judge Bean
7. "Very funny!" (2 wds.)
11. Sentimental mush
12. Nights before holidays
14. Barren
15. Pertinent
17. Grocery list entry
18. Garth Brooks's birthplace
19. Cincinnati players
20. Canyon sounds
23. Slugger Williams
25. __ plaid
26. Africa's neighbor
29. "__ Man Higgins"
30. Throbs
32. Yiddish exclamations
34. Audience cheers
36. All over again
37. Made tracks
38. Agree
40. Actor Jack
43. Steam
45. Singer __ Guthrie
46. Starbucks order
50. Dr. Frankenstein's helper
51. Harvard's rival
52. Pester
53. Pea-soupers
54. __ annum
55. Opposite of neg.

DOWN

1. Baseball team's leader (abbr.)
2. Edgar Allan __
3. Fa follower
4. Off-Broadway offering
5. Racecourse shapes
6. Strong longings
7. Style of tresses
8. Johnson of "Laugh-In"
9. Hastened
10. Naval bigwigs (abbr.)
13. Sculptor's creation
16. Harrow's rival
20. Self-esteem
21. Exclusive group
22. German gentleman
24. Sounds from a poor speaker
26. Sounds of inquiry

27. Corn cake
28. Green-___ monster
30. Gardner of "The Killers"
31. Communicate
33. Scand. land
35. Bowers
36. Farm unit
38. ___ pandowdy
39. Kitchen gadget
40. "Annie" child
41. Latin "therefore"
42. Shared online journal
44. "Stat!"
47. Tiny drink
48. Sellout inits.
49. Green-lights

Crossword 11

ACROSS

1. Tiller
5. Heredity initials
8. Weight
12. Poker fee
13. Racket or musket finish
14. Helper
15. Marries
16. Strange
18. Dwellings
20. Train terminal (abbr.)
21. Makes happen
24. Actor Haggerty
26. Kin of assoc.
27. Opp. of pos.
29. Aesop narration
33. Steeple noisemaker
35. "Obviously!"
37. Get fatter
38. Marshy inlet
40. Moses parted one
42. Neighbor of Mich.
43. Pronoun
45. Passageways
47. "Death __ Salesman" (2 wds.)
50. Exaggerate
52. Actors Perry and Modine
54. "No way, Jose!" (hyph.)
58. In a frenzy
59. Teacher's group (abbr.)
60. Starchy, edible root
61. Casino city
62. Endeavor
63. Intimation

DOWN

1. "Hee __"
2. Wind dir.
3. Inc., in England
4. Small high plateaus
5. Dethroned
6. Must have
7. Like the McDonald's logo
8. Actor Linden
9. Yale Bowl hosts
10. Level
11. Supermodel Banks
17. "Wild blue yonder" gp.
19. Big __
21. __ salad
22. Open space
23. Very unattractive
25. Pester
28. Gloomy fellow
30. Release money

31. Telephone wire
32. Finales
34. Part of L.A.
36. Relayed evidence
39. Foreboding utterance (hyph.)
41. Help
44. Happening
46. __ Carolina
47. Sharif of "Doctor Zhivago"
48. Renown
49. "This suitcase weighs __!" (2 wds.)
51. Pitcher
53. Boxing result (abbr.)
55. "Bali __"
56. Coffee server
57. Steamy

Crossword 12

ACROSS

1. Definite article
4. Auction actions
8. "__ Yeller"
11. Part of AARP (abbr.)
12. Narrow boat
13. Above, anthem-style
14. It includes "Ali Baba" (2 wds.)
17. Audit agcy.
18. Ring verdict letters
19. Gator's cousin
21. Announcer Johnny
25. Onassis, for short
26. Falsifier
30. Rover's kin
31. Stimpy's pal
32. Author Ferber et al.
34. Tiny drink
35. Pen
37. Envelope abbr.
38. Supped
39. Cure ham
41. Wallach et al.
43. Sprite
45. Laughing sound
46. "Time" et al. (2 wds.)
53. Noah's craft
54. Author Zola
55. Artist Yoko
56. Professors' helpers (abbr.)
57. Take a breather
58. Make stitches

DOWN

1. Melodic syllable
2. That girl
3. Airport monitor abbr.
4. Sheep sounds
5. Quaint hotel
6. "Stop it!"
7. Watchmaker
8. "__ la la!"
9. Lease
10. Physicians (abbr.)
12. Round shape
15. Life story, for short
16. Tiger Woods's game
19. Choicest part
20. Drummer Starr
22. Biblical peak
23. Splices film
24. Slangy refusal
25. Bowlike curves

27. Neighbor of Wyo.
28. Communal insect
29. ___ race
33. Cold symptom
36. Gets by
40. Hunter Fudd
42. Luau memento
44. Fortune's partner
45. Grind to a ___

46. Singer "King" Cole
47. Memorable years
48. Yr.'s 52
49. Boot camp residents (abbr.)
50. Thumbs-down votes
51. Compass pt.
52. Plant seed

Crossword 13

ACROSS

1. Heckle
5. "Grey's Anatomy" network
8. Cautionary word
10. Released
12. Unlawful
13. Actress Ryan
14. Sot's offense (abbr.)
15. Atlantic or Pacific
17. Half a fly
18. Sly look
20. HS course
21. Heidi of "Project Runway"
22. Highway curves
24. Makes amends
26. __-Man (video game)
28. Snow runner
29. Dame Christie of mysteries
32. Put on a show
36. Well
37. Joan of __
39. Skirt opening
40. Swimsuit top
41. "__ Gay"
43. Gardner of "Earthquake"
44. Extra dividend
46. Mutt
48. Pleasure boat
49. Harvest time
50. __ Moines
51. Darkens

DOWN

1. Misrepresents
2. Astound
3. "Othello" bad guy
4. Track down
5. Train schedule abbr.
6. Mr. Bailey of the comics
7. Poll
8. Rhythm-and-__
9. Actress Verdugo
10. Fish feature
11. Judge
12. Inactive
16. Representatives (abbr.)
19. Cancel a loan
21. Uses yarn

23. Won at musical chairs (2 wds.)
25. Finds acceptable
27. Actor-stuntman Jackie
29. Overseas
30. Fleeting look
31. Odor
33. Warning devices
34. Granted
35. Footnote abbr.

36. Ann's advice-giving twin
38. Cumulus or cirrus
41. Superlative suffix
42. Opposed
45. Sounds of hesitation
47. Wrigley's product

Crossword 14

ACROSS
1. Extremity
5. Vegas intro
8. Candidate, for short
11. Bite persistently
12. Various items (abbr.)
13. Edwards, for one (abbr.)
14. Mata __
15. Designates
17. Postal abbr.
19. Last-year students (abbr.)
20. Frontier bar
23. Apiece
26. Benchmark (abbr.)
27. Author Bagnold
29. Shout at sea
31. Retained
33. Born
34. Reference
35. Listen
36. Scored 100%
38. Bandleader Brown
39. French couturier
41. He shouts "bam!"
43. Join together

45. Polar sight
46. "Milk" star (2 wds.)
50. Sunning results
54. Danson or Koppel
55. Cassini of fashion
56. Original thought
57. Pod inhabitant
58. Snapple ingredient
59. Fidgety

DOWN
1. E followers
2. "Strangers __ Train" (2 wds.)
3. Rowing implement
4. Spin a baton
5. Gloss recipient
6. Vipers
7. Twenty years
8. Broiling __
9. Frequently, to Keats
10. Weight measures (abbr.)
12. "Evita" movie actress
16. Author Asimov
18. Antagonist
20. Spirited horse
21. Stevenson who ran against Eisenhower
22. Family member
24. Tex-Mex favorite

25. "Heartbreak __"
26. Moviegoer's admonition
28. Judging
30. "Sure!"
32. Slather with syrup
37. New Year's Eve mo.
40. Transplant
42. Fasten again
44. Remove, in editing
46. It's the "racers' edge"
47. Width of Shaq's shoes
48. Tooth-pullers' gp.
49. Teacher's group (abbr.)
51. Find a total
52. Opposite of pos.
53. Vocalize

Crossword 15

ACROSS

1. Crone
4. Teensy
7. Blob
11. Excavated material
12. Army deserter (abbr.)
13. Grad, for short
14. Vinegar's partner
15. Twiggy's skirt
16. Puppy's bites
17. Singer LaBelle
19. Burn balm
21. Dutch cheese
24. "__ for You" (2 wds.)
27. Chops
30. Slant
32. "People __ Funny"
33. Tankard fillers
34. Psychic's letters
35. Place or James
36. Address book abbr.
37. Elevations (abbr.)
38. Pupil's locale
39. Steering devices
41. Baseball's Berra
43. Highest points
45. Filly's sound

49. Supermarket stock
51. Bible twin
54. Bambi's mom, e.g.
55. Letters between A and F
56. Covers
57. __ loss (2 wds.)
58. Personal hero
59. Partner of "to"
60. Soak (up)

DOWN

1. __ skirt
2. Operatic melody
3. Dreidel stakes
4. 1910s conflict (abbr.)
5. Ages and ages
6. Director Kazan
7. __ the world (2 wds.)
8. Separate
9. Eat
10. Some sweater sizes (abbr.)
12. Among
18. Actress Harper
20. Fleur-de-__
22. Brother of Cain
23. Slightly unclear
25. Morsels
26. Shipbuilding wood
27. Old time "have"

Crossword

28. Robert ___ of Va. (2 wds.)
29. On Easy Street (hyph.)
31. Lhasa ___
35. Falco or Adams
37. Cleo's snake
40. One who poses
42. African antelopes
44. ___-serve

46. Miss Lupino et al.
47. ___ Jail (Monopoly square, 2 wds.)
48. Rubbish pile
49. "Most Wanted" org.
50. Problem for TV's Monk (abbr.)
52. ___ Lancelot
53. Bother

Crossword 16

ACROSS

1. __ jerky
5. Mild exclamation
8. Over
12. Thomas __ Edison
13. Consume food
14. Neeson of "Run All Night"
15. FBI figure (hyph.)
16. New Deal agency (abbr.)
17. Fun-house shrieks
18. Wager money
20. Truck-producer's inits.
22. Canters
25. Commoner, once
29. Milky stones
30. Train systs.
31. __ Miguel
32. Abrasive material
33. Golf prop
34. "It's __ to Tell a Lie" (2 wds.)
35. Actor Holm
36. Extreme anger
37. Higher in rank
38. Register at the Hilton (2 wds.)
40. Lined with cloth
41. With it
42. Coffee maker
43. Rude person
46. Wooden nail
48. Snug rooms
52. German car
53. Snaky swimmer
54. Possesses
55. Expires
56. Needing water
57. Salamander

DOWN

1. Groceries holder
2. Shade source
3. Mendes or Longoria
4. Engine part (2 wds.)
5. Lady's companion
6. Corn piece
7. Furniture with shelves
8. Baldwin et al.
9. Attachment
10. Hardwood tree
11. Evening hrs.
19. Curvy letter
21. Moms
22. Reasoning
23. Book club lady
24. Author Thomas

25. Spruce up
26. Org.
27. Artless
28. Blended colors
33. Stumbled
34. Desert
36. Dwight's nickname
37. Where Zimbabwe is (abbr.)

39. Actor Sarandon
42. Repulsive
43. Evil
44. Parisian agreement
45. Wordsworth work
47. Bard's "always"
49. Bleating mom
50. Wind dir.
51. Concorde's inits.

Crossword 17

ACROSS

1. African nation
5. Closest pal, to a texter
8. Prompt
12. Contain
13. Yahoo! rival
14. Associate
15. Valentine phrase (3 wds.)
17. Bread for hummus
18. Absorbent cloth
19. Jar top
21. Erich ___ Stroheim
22. Nero's language (abbr.)
24. Wine's companion
26. Registers for a course
30. Bungles
33. Summon via pager
34. Civil War gp.
36. In apple pie order
37. Single stroke over par
39. Student
41. Locality
43. Pothole filler
44. ___ and grill
46. Beverage suffix
48. ___ Janeiro (2 wds.)
52. Alan or Robert
54. "Holy" fish
56. West et al.
57. Retiree's acct.
58. Black and pekoe
59. Famous Verdi opera
60. Blasting substance (abbr.)
61. Jedi teacher

DOWN

1. Voucher
2. Angel's aura
3. Acknowledge
4. Real estate tycoon
5. Howl
6. Swindle
7. Liquid
8. Interval
9. Italian export (2 wds.)
10. Choir singer
11. Actress Cannon
16. Airline to Ben-Gurion (2 wds.)
20. Search for fossils
23. Special treatment, for short
25. Renown
26. ___ and flow
27. Modern (prefix)
28. Inspected

29. Draft agcy.
31. Drug-regulating org.
32. Neighbor of Israel (abbr.)
35. Perform on stage
38. Affirmative vote
40. Listen attentively
42. Grant entrance
44. Home of the Crimson

Tide, for short
45. Jai ___
47. Acquire through work
49. Chocolate sandwich cookie
50. Expired
51. Movie lioness
53. Big ___ whale (2 wds.)
55. Purring creature

Crossword 18

ACROSS

1. Tobacco plug
5. Bro or sis
8. German exclamation
11. Israeli dance
12. Know-it-__
14. Meadow noise
15. Former Apple rivals
16. Theatrical sketch
17. Ted Danson TV show
18. Sports announcer Bob
20. Less spicy, as salsa
22. Biblical judge
23. Arafat's organization (abbr.)
24. Talk in the library
28. Brass instruments
32. Hesitating sounds
33. Lamb's dad
35. Candle count
36. Rhythm
39. Milliner's workplace (2 wds.)
42. French friend
44. "Kindergarten __"
45. Not as worked up
48. Voters' structures
52. Sound of discovery
53. Confer
55. Actress Patricia
56. Mom, to some
57. "Be that __ may..." (2 wds.)
58. Rowlands of film
59. Six-pack muscles, informally
60. Chuckle sound
61. Small whirlpool

DOWN

1. "Vogue" adjective
2. Vagabond
3. Arsenal's inventory
4. Expends needlessly
5. More impudent
6. Sort
7. Dirigible
8. Alphabet start
9. Pillow covering
10. Salon sweepings
13. Avocet's kin
19. High mountain
21. Reed or Jacobi
24. Soaking
25. Ancient kingdom (abbr.)
26. Doctrine's suffix

27. Pep squad's word
29. What Scrooge shouted
30. Gone by
31. Labor Day mo.
34. Shakespearean play
37. Actress Dawber
38. From alpha to __
40. Besides
41. Absorbent cleaning aid

43. "When __ Eyes..."
45. Unconscious state
46. "Moby-Dick" captain
47. Highs and __
49. __ off (irate)
50. Farm employee
51. Destroy
54. Fight

Crossword 19

ACROSS

1. Presidential nickname
4. Current indication
8. Pvt.'s superior
11. Kin (abbr.)
12. Female title
14. Fish story
15. Flee
16. U.S. folklore
18. What Glade covers
20. Radar screen image
21. PC connection letters
23. Unpunctual
25. Farm unit
28. Staff member
31. Heredity inits.
33. Bombshell West
34. Wrong guess
35. Pt. of speech
36. Taxpayer's ID
37. __ Antony
38. Church wing
39. Seasoning
41. __ Na Na
43. Romances
45. Third planet
49. Sulfur
53. Colgate's competition
54. German article
55. Dieter's fare
56. L followers
57. Scrambled item
58. Uncle __ rice
59. Fathers

DOWN

1. A Guthrie
2. Rosary unit
3. "Sesame Street" favorite
4. Pile up
5. Word before shaft or corder
6. He took the reins from HST
7. Starchy food, informally
8. Empty talk
9. Tailor's tool
10. Grassland
13. It-girl Sienna
17. "Alias" gp.
19. Be sorry
22. Vamp Theda
24. Loose __
25. Morning hours (abbr.)
26. Way to pay
27. Beginning again

29. Discount rack abbr.
30. Severinsen and Holliday
32. Roadway (abbr.)
34. Decorate in relief
38. Letters on some tow trucks
40. CD-___

42. Pays attention
44. Brief try
46. Sloping roadway
47. Nancy Sinatra's sister
48. Managed-care gps.
49. Queen or drone
50. Fix, as a game
51. Barcelona "rah"
52. Fabray, for short

Crossword 20

ACROSS

1. Songwriter Berlin, familiarly
4. Neglects
9. "__ Abner"
12. Me, to Miss Piggy
13. Juliet's lover
14. List-ending abbr.
15. Sunday talk (abbr.)
16. Deserted
18. "__ milk?"
20. Singer Cooke
21. Apparent
25. Certain NCO
29. Brooches
30. Sandy's bark
32. Actress Donna
33. Physics, e.g. (abbr.)
34. "Lenore" author
35. Table part
36. Give approval
38. Fa follower
39. Chip brand
40. Excavations
42. Made happy
44. "Annabel __"
46. Barbecue residue
47. Amusement park transport (2 wds.)
52. Unaffiliated voter (abbr.)
55. Authors' submissions (abbr.)
56. Designer Calvin
57. "...borrower __ a lender be"
58. Scored more points
59. Faxes
60. Wildebeest

DOWN

1. Says "howdy" through AOL, perhaps
2. Fish eggs
3. Richmond native
4. Speak before an audience
5. Disorderly crowd
6. "__ Loser" (2 wds.)
7. Lacrosse teams
8. Carbonated drinks
9. Dawson or Cariou
10. Adherent (suffix)
11. Calculator display (abbr.)
17. Epps or Sharif
19. Medicates too much (abbr.)
21. __ Downs
22. Lawrence of "Mama's Family"

23. Afternoon siestas
24. Scout group
26. Greatly enjoying
27. Goslings, e.g.
28. Bordered
31. Cut, as a tree
37. Dog's sound
39. Had existence
41. Hunts for

43. Makes money
45. Writer Gardner
47. German car inits.
48. GI's social club
49. Hotmail provider (abbr.)
50. 100 years (abbr.)
51. Assist
53. French negative
54. Actress Joanne

Crossword 21

ACROSS

1. A Baldwin brother
5. English fliers (abbr.)
8. Jazz jobs
12. __ the Clown
13. House extension
14. Caesar's city
15. Underwater cadge
17. Art course (abbr.)
18. Comic Sandler et al.
19. Very pale
21. Computer key
23. Paid attention
27. TV station
31. Writing that is worthless
32. Comics' Alley __
33. __ Gatos
35. Pen-making name
36. Catholic leaders
39. Cookie brand
42. Be witness (to)
44. Astronaut Grissom
45. Play area
47. Counterfeit
51. Mafia chief
54. Space beyond the baseball diamond
56. Part of U.S.A. (abbr.)
57. Schedule abbr.
58. In eager desire
59. Calendar number
60. Compass letters
61. Gordie of hockey

DOWN

1. Swedish rock group
2. Cargo
3. Poet Pound
4. Flimflam artists
5. Family __ room
6. "...__ good night" (2 wds.)
7. __ and blood
8. Ashier
9. Charged atom
10. A.M. show, briefly
11. Tennis term
16. Org.
20. __ up (excited)
22. Animation collectible
24. Kid's "reservation"
25. Heroic poem
26. Art __
27. __ plea (2 wds.)
28. A __ and a holler

29. Abbr. on a schedule
30. Chaney of films
34. Hang loosely
37. Pooh's pal
38. Govt. agcy.
40. Polish
41. Old Testament prophet
43. Hurries
46. Names
48. ___-mutton (hyph.)
49. Like a snail
50. Margin
51. Rogue
52. Drs.' gp.
53. House animal
55. Edison's monogram

Crossword 22

ACROSS

1. TV monitoring gp.
4. Game fish
8. __ bomb
12. Hot-tubbing sound
13. Newspaper article
14. Not easy
15. "__ Lost You"
16. Pretentious one's "bye-bye"
17. Mimi, Nicole, and Katie to Tom Cruise
18. Cash in coupons
20. Large quantity
22. Dummy
23. Dandy
24. Extends across
26. Where Munich is (abbr.)
27. Sot's conviction (abbr.)
30. Boater's blades
31. Apr.'s season
32. Twosomes
33. Central Park location (abbr.)
34. AWOL pursuers
35. Trotting horse
36. Western Native American
38. Deplaned
39. Make believe
40. __ the point
43. Sense
44. Drink for Juan
46. Jerky motion
47. Ill-at-__
48. __ of living
49. Tennis shot
50. __ Rabbit
51. Garden shed tools
52. "Oz" aunt and others

DOWN

1. Nothing special
2. Hibernation spot
3. Alternative to American (2 wds.)
4. Muscleman's pride
5. "__ to Kill" (2 wds.)
6. Baltic, e.g.
7. Seethe
8. In front
9. Like most donations (hyph.)
10. Crude minerals
11. Hospital figs.
19. Geologic periods
21. "__ Day Will Come"

24. JFK, to Joe
25. Stipend
26. Certain doctors (abbr.)
28. Heartache
29. Tel Aviv's land (abbr.)
31. Popeye's favorite
32. Raised platform
34. Car buyer's concern

(abbr.)
35. Folds of cloth
37. Tank ship
38. Treat badly
39. Terror
41. Adverse fate
42. Abates
43. Winter mo.
45. Sentimental mush

Crossword 23

ACROSS

1. Double this to get a dance
4. Hawaiian food
7. Johann Sebastian __
11. Pig with tusks
12. GI's address (abbr.)
13. Singer Fitzgerald
14. Disintegrated
16. Cracked, as a door
17. Dover's state (abbr.)
18. Jeans fabric
20. Ottawa's prov.
21. Part of PG
23. "Star Trek" doctor
26. Letter start (2 wds.)
29. Over yonder
30. 2003 movie "Agent __ Banks"
31. Swindle (2 wds.)
35. Logic
36. Went around
38. Expert aviator
40. Owner's proof
41. Exclamation of discovery
44. Myrna Loy's "Thin Man" role
46. Appreciative
48. Mend socks
49. Race an engine
50. LAX postings
51. Corset stiffener
52. Prior, to poets
53. Wee one

DOWN

1. Hub
2. Tote
3. Biceps site
4. Dimmer
5. Made the first bet
6. Wash for wounds
7. "Don't __ stranger!" (2 wds.)
8. "Mammy" singer (2 wds.)
9. Scottish group
10. Stag
11. A trailers
15. Personal calendar abbr.
19. NYC transit line
21. Food fish
22. Like the McDonald's logo
23. Comic Bernie
24. Corporate bigwig

(abbr.)

25. Capital of Australia

27. Proofs of age, for short

28. Bread type

32. Relevant

33. ___ d'hotel

34. Old Testament queen

35. Observed

37. "12 Years a ___"

38. No ifs, ___, or buts

39. Layer of paint

41. '60s hairdo

42. Emotionally wounded

43. Pacino et al.

45. Whatever

47. "Krazy" one of cartoons

Crossword 24

ACROSS

1. Cereal ingredient
4. BB's, e.g.
8. Pres. Coolidge
11. __ carte (2 wds.)
12. Couch
13. Yiddish exclamations
14. Made Mom a picture in preschool
17. Vinyl records (abbr.)
18. Stooge with bangs
19. "__ a Feeling" (2 wds.)
21. Shaving mishaps
25. Shivering one's sound
26. Amateur radio operators
30. Milk (Fr.)
31. "Norma __"
32. __ change
34. Course (abbr.)
35. "__ girl!"
37. La Salle of "ER"
38. Dog doc
39. Did business
41. Takes advantage of
43. "... a man __ mouse?" (2 wds.)
45. Ceiling spinner
46. Police collection of crooks' photos (2 wds.)
53. Electrical unit (abbr.)
54. Requirements
55. Hawaiian instrument, for short
56. Arnold Palmer's gp.
57. Hamlet, e.g.
58. Decompose

DOWN

1. Fellow lacking grace
2. "The Greatest"
3. Light brown
4. Exposes
5. Best on a team (abbr.)
6. Sir's counterpart
7. Hamburger garnish
8. Portable bed
9. Gob's reply
10. Psychedelic drug (abbr.)
12. The __ of despair
15. Day-__ (fluorescent product)
16. Singer Diamond
19. All steamed up
20. Garbo of films
22. Slice turkey
23. Flying toys
24. Proofreading comment
25. Headless nail

27. King Kong, e.g.
28. Deface
29. ___ Lanka
33. Adds up to
36. Matty of baseball
40. Fashion
42. Weekend comedy show, for short
44. On the briny

45. Lose color
46. Bang a gavel
47. Texter's "wow!"
48. College student's concern (abbr.)
49. Patton's rank (abbr.)
50. Belgium's cont.
51. "Citizen Kane" movie studio
52. Until now

Crossword 25

ACROSS

1. Cable choice (abbr.)
5. Navy VIP (abbr.)
8. Low milit. rank
11. Jr., often
12. __ Brummel
14. MGM's lion
15. Diminutive suffix
16. Atop
17. From __ Z (2 wds.)
18. Skater Katarina
20. Conclusive
22. Plato's city
25. Between (prefix)
26. Labors
27. Construction route
30. Ticked off
31. Lawmaker (abbr.)
32. Pregrown lawn
34. Actress Reynolds
37. Mr. Claus
39. Hither and __
40. Purple flowers
41. Not as outgoing
44. Bartlett's kin
45. Served as guide
46. Greek sandwich
48. Auto pioneer
52. Pub order
53. Greek god of love
54. Outlet
55. Gore and Biden, e.g. (abbr.)
56. Scand. land
57. Peron and Gabor

DOWN

1. Revolutionary Guevara
2. Fish trap
3. Fragment
4. __ embroidery
5. Borders on
6. Co. section
7. Chairman __
8. Blueprint, e.g.
9. Greek salad cheese
10. Moderately cold
13. Lacking qualifications
19. Those holding office
21. Bride's reply (2 wds.)
22. 24-hour teller (abbr.)
23. Froglike creature
24. Lie low
25. Bachelors
27. Sandra of "Gidget"
28. Annapolis school (abbr.)
29. College military gp.

31. Religious offense
33. Prosecutors (abbr.)
35. "Au revoir!"
36. Entertainer Victor
37. Haley, to Luke Dunphy
38. Wall recess
40. Unbound
41. Balkan native
42. Give support

43. The ___ of March
44. Forehead
47. Decade segments (abbr.)
49. Bk. after Exodus
50. Basis of heredity (abbr.)
51. Wall and Sesame (abbr.)

Crossword 26

ACROSS
1. Witch
4. Gin and __
9. Satchel
12. Sooner than, poetically
13. Advantage
14. Go wrong
15. "Give __ break!" (2 wds.)
16. TV's Couric
17. Wallach or Whitney
18. Jerusalem's land
20. Fang injection
22. "__ Miniver"
23. Florida's Bush
24. Fellows
27. Seaports
31. Half a fly
32. Emeril's exclamation
33. A, __, U and sometimes Y
34. Overstuffed footstool
37. __ in the ocean (tiny bit)
39. The Gulf __
40. Funnyman Caesar
41. Telephones
44. Directions

48. Beerlike brew
49. Abhorred
52. Charged atom
53. Fix, as a game
54. Senior
55. Greek consonant
56. Classic car
57. Hoarse
58. TV __

DOWN
1. Half (prefix)
2. Son of Hera
3. Toothed wheel
4. Opposite of givers
5. Ellipses
6. King Cole or Turner
7. Clock's three
8. Skillful
9. Existed
10. Folkie Guthrie
11. Bleak
19. Total (abbr.)
21. Subside
23. Traffic congestion
24. Classic racecar, for short
25. Guess at a price (abbr.)
26. Butterfly __
27. Chewbacca pal Solo
28. Above, to a poet

29. "__ Rita"
30. Use a paper towel
32. Taproom
35. Hooter
36. Potato-crushing device
37. Hang laundry on the line (2 wds.)
38. Ike's monogram
40. High-priced
41. Author John Dickson

42. "__ of the Mind" (2 wds.)
43. Maker of little blocks
45. Flask sips
46. Measured amount
47. Irritated state
50. Fla.'s neighbor
51. Grid coups (abbr.)

Crossword 27

ACROSS

1. Lawyer's gp.
4. Snapshot, briefly
7. Test-driver's car
11. __ Kong
13. "Memoirs __ Geisha" (2 wds.)
14. Cable sports network
15. Musical about Don Quixote (4 wds.)
18. Make a mistake disappear
19. Ayres et al.
20. Sock part
22. Lay off (2 wds.)
26. Dental gp.
29. Dash's partner
30. Racetrack's boundary
31. Comedian Hope
32. Snooty people
35. "Mayberry, __"
36. "Fargo" filmmaker Joel or Ethan
38. Cake baker's need
39. Main and Elm (abbr.)
40. Night vision
42. Lupino, Tarbell, and Cantor

44. Surrender
46. Stallone role
50. NBA no-no (2 wds.)
54. __ extra cost (2 wds.)
55. Homer's wholesome neighbor
56. Fitzgerald of jazz
57. Soup containers
58. Snaky sound
59. Pixie

DOWN

1. "Alas!" (2 wds.)
2. Wild hog
3. "__ Karenina"
4. Candidate (abbr.)
5. Patsy Cline hit (4 wds.)
6. Was present at
7. More compact
8. Computer exit (abbr.)
9. Dashboard abbr.
10. "Design __ Dime" (2 wds.)
12. "Gracious!"
16. Gives sustenance
17. Leatherworker's punch
21. A mighty long time
23. Gobs
24. Birthday __
25. Name in autos

26. Alphabet start
27. Entrance
28. Busy as ___ (2 wds.)
33. Naughty
34. Angry growl
37. Mexican restaurant offering
41. TV's "Mad ___"
43. Baseball call

45. Uproars
47. Tunneling animal
48. Calf's father
49. Lovable "Frozen" character
50. Tic-___-toe
51. Airport monitor abbr.
52. Anderson Cooper's channel
53. Sitcom interrupters

Crossword 28

ACROSS

1. __ bargain
5. Male antelope
9. Film studio inits.
12. Radiator sound
13. Curly hairdo
14. Sept. preceder
15. Bandleader Arnaz
16. Doves' sounds
17. Hotel offerings (abbr.)
18. Copacetic (hyph.)
20. Bonzo, for one
22. Chronicles
25. Magda's sister
26. Onassis, for short
27. Decompose
28. Memento
31. Price markers
33. Prankster's plot
35. Weighty work
36. Detest
38. Spanish "Mrs."
40. Champagne producer __ Pérignon
41. Angle starter
42. Grasper
44. Bards
46. Popular Nintendo product
47. Buzz __
48. Summits
50. Cavort
54. Long-running comedy show (abbr.)
55. Son of Isaac
56. Gets one's __ (annoys)
57. Pack animal
58. Inclined runway
59. Omar of "House"

DOWN

1. Advanced degree (abbr.)
2. Pinocchio's nose extender
3. Snaky shape
4. From China
5. In-box filler
6. Alien's ride (abbr.)
7. Gator's cousin
8. Proper
9. Bread spread
10. Forrest played by Tom Hanks
11. Booker T. and the __
19. Rowing implement
21. "Big Daddy" Burl
22. Kuwait native

23. Late-show viewers (2 wds.)
24. Store for future use
26. __ moment's notice (2 wds.)
29. Composer Stravinsky
30. Rotating machine part
32. Furious
34. Matures (2 wds.)

37. Singer Tex
39. Frazier's rival
43. Mournful song
44. Cooking vessels
45. Former Cub Sammy
47. Govt. agcy.
49. Tennis's Shriver
51. Alley __ of the comics
52. AAA giveaway
53. Parts of qts.

Crossword 29

ACROSS

1. Corporate bigwig (abbr.)
4. "The More You Know" network
7. Cooking grease
10. Drag along
12. Where to go for a tow (abbr.)
13. Old King __
14. Comic Johnson
15. Deface
16. No ifs, __, or buts
17. Wish
19. Evans et al.
21. "__ Rhythm" (2 wds.)
22. "Are you a man __ mouse?" (2 wds.)
23. Lucille Ball was one
26. Record __
30. Miner's paydirt
31. Berlin's locale (abbr.)
33. "__ recall..." (2 wds.)
34. Singer Bobby
37. Observed
40. Grazing locale
42. __ beds
43. Nations' military forces
46. Bell tower
49. Bill
50. Pronoun
52. General Robert __ (2 wds.)
53. Morsel
54. Germany's cont.
55. Dye
56. Distance measures (abbr.)
57. Lgs.' opposites (abbr.)
58. Taro dish

DOWN

1. Lowe or Everett
2. Bus ticket price
3. Alien
4. Class reunion label
5. Sheep's cry
6. Monte __
7. Devoted
8. Hawkeye's portrayer
9. Actress Harper
11. Actress Vivien
13. Artificial waterway
18. __ v. Wade
20. George Gershwin's brother
23. Shaft
24. Age

25. Study
27. Gymnastics move
28. Application
29. Way or point start
32. Burglars
35. "___ Ike" (2 wds.)
36. Society column "born"
38. Week part (abbr.)

39. Lakeshore's recess
41. Dolts
43. Ann's advice-giving twin
44. Actor Tim ("WKRP")
45. Small rugs
47. Divorce city
48. Sasquatch's cousin
51. Ho-___

Crossword 30

ACROSS

1. TV series set in Vegas
4. __ plea (2 wds.)
8. Self-importance
11. Sharp desires
13. Pro votes
14. Clamor
15. Hamlet, e.g.
16. Lake Geneva peaks
17. "__ to Extremes" (Billy Joel, 2 wds.)
18. After LBJ
20. Football kicks
22. Somber
25. Moore of "Ghost"
26. Resubscribe
27. St. Patrick's home
31. Author Fleming
32. Shed tears
33. Herd sound
34. Period when there's a lack of water
37. Strength
39. Kill
40. Wash lightly
41. Submarine-detecting device
43. Rock's __ Fighters
44. Graceful tree
45. Frenzy
47. File folders' features
51. Mauna __
52. Writer Ferber
53. Eject
54. Easter's season (abbr.)
55. OT book (abbr.)
56. Postal delivery path (abbr.)

DOWN

1. Charisse of "Brigadoon"
2. Bering __
3. "Holiday __"
4. "Misery" star James
5. Surname of Popeye's girlfriend
6. Spicy
7. Leap to conclusions
8. Fix a manuscript
9. Jazz jobs
10. "Sail __ Ship of State!" (2 wds.)
12. Put into play
19. Cat's sound
21. None whatsoever
22. Boxed chart
23. Back section
24. __ Domini

Crossword

25. Soiled
28. "___ for All Seasons" (2 wds.)
29. "___ the Time to Fall in Love"
30. Completed
32. Pretense
35. Milit. branch
36. Looked at angrily
37. JFK, to RFK
38. Rampages
41. Pig food
42. Sharif or Bradley
43. Exploit
44. City railways
46. Wildebeest
48. Month to pay the IRS
49. Play the ponies
50. Scand. land

Crossword 31

ACROSS

1. Love foolishly
5. Rum cake
9. Thurman of "Kill Bill"
12. Author Haley
13. "Oh, sure!" (2 wds.)
14. Uncooked
15. Car sound
16. Disown
18. Gremlin co.
20. CPR expert
21. "Hard-Hearted __"
24. Little devils
28. Destroy slowly
29. Pen company
30. Supper scrap
31. Skill
32. Workout cushion
33. Goat's sound
34. CD-__
35. Crow's kin
36. Brownish-yellow
38. Some Scandinavians
40. Motorless aircraft
41. Last mo.
42. "Holy cow!," online
43. Deli selection
47. "Heavenly" instrument
51. Like some as-is garments (abbr.)
52. "__ Brockovich"
53. Makes do
54. Some office equipment (abbr.)
55. "Rats!"
56. Captivated

DOWN

1. Apply sparingly
2. Bullfight bellow
3. Ball-propping gadget
4. Grow bigger, as a business
5. White tree
6. Honest __ Lincoln
7. Profit
8. Type of modern power
9. Coffeepot
10. Raincoat, for short
11. Reverence
17. Shoshonean
19. West of Hollywood
21. Pays attention
22. Robin Hood's weapon
23. "I didn't do it!" (2 wds.)
25. Pastoral wanderer

26. Duckling's daddy
27. Case or well preceder
29. __ rum
32. Cosmetic kit staple
35. Showed derision
36. Alphabetic trio
37. More lofty
39. Banned insecticide (abbr.)

40. Auctioneer's cry
43. Card spot
44. __ de Triomphe
45. Upperclassmen (abbr.)
46. 1/60 of an hr.
48. Rap sheet initials
49. Agent (abbr.)
50. Attention-getting hiss

Crossword 32

ACROSS

1. Chuckle sound
4. Movie meanie
8. Eddie Cantor's wife
11. Compass heading
12. Type of drum
13. Spielberg, e.g. (abbr.)
14. Elton John's title
15. Reviewer Roger
16. Yellowstone animal
17. Barbie, e.g.
19. Housetop feature
21. Shepherd's __
23. Min. part
24. Sculptor's tools
28. __ Stanley Gardner
32. Through
33. Rug's location
36. Boxer Norton
37. Kong's buddies
39. Errors
41. Drama division
44. Tint
45. Psychologist McGraw (2 wds.)
48. Exclamations
51. Compete
52. Skirt style (hyph.)
54. Ring win (abbr.)
56. Quiet __ mouse (2 wds.)
57. Dreads
58. Have the flu
59. Bruins' gp.
60. Columnist Bombeck
61. Ford midsize car

DOWN

1. "__ a Rebel"
2. Author Bagnold
3. Medal winner
4. Mass
5. Draft status (hyph.)
6. Fiona and Shrek
7. "The Hunchback of __ Dame"
8. Brain creation
9. Kind of pickle
10. "Raiders of the Lost __"
12. Faith
18. Vinyl records (abbr.)
20. Rink necessity
22. Building addition
24. Number-cruncher (abbr.)
25. With it
26. Vexation
27. __ sister

29. Astaire's studio
30. MGM lion
31. USN officer (abbr.)
34. Aah's partner
35. Applies color to the cheeks
38. Practical joker's patsy
40. Quilting event
42. Irritate

43. Roofer
45. Chef's creation
46. Not fake
47. Neeson of films
49. List shortener (2 wds.)
50. Comedy sketch
51. Vincent __ Gogh
53. Gp. once headed by Heston
55. "__ Black Magic"

Crossword 33

ACROSS

1. Modeling material
5. Enjoy taffy
9. Rotter
12. Off-white
13. Locality
14. "Ben __"
15. UV blocker
17. Gobbled up
18. Snaky swimmer
19. Pitch
21. Stop
24. Mrs., in Berlin
26. Jolson et al.
27. Thugs
31. Greek salad ingredient
33. Sea inlet
34. Pronto
35. Exalted rank
37. Supplement
38. Sommer of "The Prize"
39. Was mistaken
41. Angry expression
44. Rush
45. Internet access provider (abbr.)
46. Winning by a nose
(2 wds.)
52. Follower (suffix)
53. Loud laugh
54. That being the case (2 wds.)
55. Ph.D. or B.A.
56. Harvard's rival
57. Doctor's word for "quick"

DOWN

1. Home of "Survivor"
2. Baseball legend Gehrig
3. Actress Sothern
4. Affirmatives
5. Rob Reiner's dad
6. Ancient kingdom (abbr.)
7. Wide loafer width
8. Classified item (2 wds.)
9. Burn slightly
10. Ford product
11. Teen sleuth Nancy
16. Before dee
20. Wahine's dance
21. Supper club
22. Type of school (abbr.)
23. Italian wine town
24. "May the __ be with you"

Crossword

25. Italy's capital
27. Quantity of yarn
28. Internet surfer
29. Produce
30. Zoomed
32. Over again
36. Detective Queen
39. Berlin one
40. Celeb Philbin

41. Spoke
42. Enclosure for sheep
43. Cassini of fashion
44. Add to the staff
47. ___ number on (2 wds.)
48. Lass
49. Frequently, in poems
50. "Born in the ___"
51. Child

Crossword 34

ACROSS

1. Place with fighter jets (abbr.)
4. "Mamma Mia!" group
8. __ Diego Padres
11. Producer Ziegfeld, to friends
12. Simon's "Plaza __"
14. Bowler's target
15. Noon eating locale
17. Lemon beverage
18. Swiss peak
19. D-H connectors
21. Smart
23. Shore and Washington
26. Tall and thin
27. Julie of "Mary Poppins"
29. Sandy's sound
30. Paycheck abbr.
31. Coal pitch
32. Carpenter's tote (2 wds.)
35. "Same here!"
37. Warm __ (air masses)
38. Yalies
39. Me, to Miss Piggy
40. 100%
41. Double this to get a dance
43. Big moment for Baby (2 wds.)
49. '70s band Steely __
50. 1996 Madonna film
51. Way back when
52. Pose
53. Son of Seth
54. Movie ratings (abbr.)

DOWN

1. Labor organization (abbr.)
2. Grippe
3. Singer Jon __ Jovi
4. Actress Elizabeth
5. Baby's feeding finale
6. Life's story, informally
7. From __ Z (2 wds.)
8. Favorite pasta
9. Help
10. Compass letters
13. Rewrite
16. Keg
20. Wide's partner
21. __ 1812 (2 wds.)
22. Leak source
23. Bodice tucks
24. Election winners

25. Smacks
26. Map marking (abbr.)
28. Sellout inits.
30. Clobber
33. 18th-century card game
34. Spoon's tablemate
35. Burke and others
36. Evils
40. Regarding (2 wds.)
41. Bank offerings (abbr.)
42. "Bali __"
44. "__ Got a Secret"
45. "__ Tin Tin"
46. Strike gently
47. Hen product
48. Opposite of negative (abbr.)

Crossword 35

ACROSS

1. English TV network
4. Cause to swell
9. Wither
12. Friend of Winnie-the-Pooh
13. Lexus rival
14. Start of a cheer
15. Besides
16. Jerk
17. Causes of bounced checks (abbr.)
18. Negotiate
20. Investigate
22. Claim on property
25. Actress Charlotte __
26. Mixes playing cards
30. Apartment house, e.g. (abbr.)
33. Topeka's st.
34. Talent
36. Woolly mama
37. "__ Love Again" (2 wds.)
39. Glorious
41. Businesses (abbr.)
43. Lone
44. Actress Mills
46. "__ Ideas" (2 wds.)
49. Abbr. on a timetable
50. Frequently
53. Address bk. abbr.
55. Foil material
56. Employee's hope
57. Herbal drink
58. Army-base figs.
59. Shoe stretchers
60. Elec. measure

DOWN

1. Bikini part
2. Spy James
3. Zip __
4. Officer of the court
5. Digital watch display (abbr.)
6. Yes, to Pierre
7. Baseball nickname (hyph.)
8. Spud
9. Removed snow
10. Military staffer
11. Certain doctors (abbr.)
19. Candidate Landon
21. Chemist's workshop
23. House additions
24. Certain tides
26. Snow runner
27. Lunch meat

28. Mythical, one-horned creatures
29. Farm's tower
31. Sot's conviction (abbr.)
32. Diploma alternative (abbr.)
35. Recovers the inside
38. Prefix meaning not
40. Opp. of pos.
42. Nasal sound
44. Annoying faucet noise
45. In the distance
47. Place or James
48. Pour
49. Bank amenity (abbr.)
51. Equal score
52. Wind direction (abbr.)
54. Friendly cat's perch

Crossword 36

ACROSS

1. Pulsate
6. Little pellets
9. Phrase in a beach town's advertising (2 wds.)
10. Reviewer Ebert
13. Machine for pressing
14. Acquire
16. Problem for TV's Monk (abbr.)
17. Actresses Stimson and Gilbert
19. Train stop (abbr.)
20. __ of Tonkin
22. Youngster
23. Hop
24. Threw rocks at
26. Compass indications (abbr.)
27. Neighbor of Syria (abbr.)
28. Baseball's Maglie
29. Lightless
31. Variety of melon
34. Annoying fellow
35. Contained
36. Canary's home
38. Behind, on a boat
39. Stateswoman Meir
41. Refrain syllable
42. Jackie who played Uncle Fester
44. One who overacts
46. Search blindly
47. Counts, e.g.
48. __ Plaines
49. Used the slopes

DOWN

1. Oolong drinker's need
2. Drawer pull
3. Tatter
4. Some paintings
5. Large wave
6. Like an avenue
7. Curtsies
8. Cpl.'s boss
9. L.A. skyline concealer
11. Disburdener
12. Hayworth et al.
15. Snooze like a cat
18. Eliminate
21. Coquette
23. Purple flower

25. Disapprover's sound
26. Prosecutors (abbr.)
28. Makes sorrowful
29. Car heater setting
30. Actress Mary
31. Coolidge's nickname
32. "___ Hymn of the Republic"
33. Consented

34. ___-Man (arcade game)
35. Razor strops
37. All ___ (attentive)
39. Look on with astonishment
40. In a frenzy
43. "In ___ We Trust"
45. Kimono fastener

Crossword 37

ACROSS

1. Unruly gang
4. Lived
9. Hubbub
12. "Just as I thought!"
13. Roundup
14. Dream stage (abbr.)
15. Rival of Miles Standish (2 wds.)
17. "__ whillikers!"
18. Questionable
19. Rose's pricker
21. Huge person
24. Dove's call
25. Respond (abbr.)
26. Ill-at-__
29. Falco or McClurg
33. Land parcel
34. Praise
36. Locale of the Braves (abbr.)
37. Med. sch. course
39. Ultimatum word
40. JFK's party (abbr.)
41. Gives approval
43. Pretenses
45. Jailed one
48. Edible fish
50. "His master's voice" co.
51. Light musical shows
56. Exclamations of surprise
57. Ball and __
58. PPO alternative
59. Obtained
60. Sorts
61. "Yippee!"

DOWN

1. Milit. rank
2. Cry of surprise
3. Scrooge's shout
4. One who is inducted
5. "__ Hall"
6. Mary Baker __
7. Trevino or Majors
8. Scout's rider
9. Jason's ship
10. "The __ Hunter"
11. Sign of the future
16. Author Anaïs __
20. Weed digger
21. Elaborate party
22. Sharing a secret (2 wds.)
23. Nick and Nora's dog
24. Corporate VIPs
27. Hatchets

28. Insignia on a Cardinal's cap
30. Toddler word
31. Piece of gossip
32. Stately trees
35. Reduces
38. Besides
42. Strike sharply
44. FDR's follower

45. Pond croaker
46. "Little Sir ___"
47. Linger
48. Chili ingredient
49. Like the Gobi
52. Greek letter
53. Poetic "your"
54. Doctors' gp.
55. Tofu base

Crossword 38

ACROSS

1. Admiring sounds
4. Consists of
7. Swerve
11. Rent
12. Govt. agents
13. Pelt
14. Mrs., to Pierre
15. Fashion model Macpherson
16. "It's __ blur" (2 wds.)
17. Egyptian cobra
18. Parisian pal
19. Beau and Jeff's dad
20. Hockey's Bobby
22. Tempo
24. First class (2 wds.)
26. See at a distance
27. Tiny bit
30. Ornamental border
32. Cuba, e.g.
34. Trio after Q
35. Guinness or Baldwin
37. Luncheonette orders
38. Compact __ player
39. Interrogate
40. Ancient language
43. __ Palmas

45. Kenny G's instrument, for short
48. Strong __ ox (2 wds.)
49. Mata __
50. That guy
51. Existed
52. Purposes
53. Certain poem
54. Short sleeps
55. Make an attempt
56. Ashen

DOWN

1. __ mater
2. Garment edges
3. "Hurry, driver!" (3 wds.)
4. Ship's wheel
5. Improvises (hyph.)
6. Wind dir.
7. Commandments word
8. Metric measure
9. Indolently
10. With no juice, as a battery
12. Phobia
19. Installs carpeting
21. "__ and Stimpy" (cartoon)
23. Heroic narrative
24. Egypt's cont.
25. Conjunctions

Down

26. "Electric" swimmers
27. "Oprah," e.g. (2 wds.)
28. Picnic pest
29. Cavity filler's deg.
31. Win
33. Pounds (abbr.)
36. Filled pastry
38. Wines and ___ (treats royally)
39. Having no warranty (2 wds.)
40. ___ mower
41. Out of port
42. Infield cover, informally
44. The Salvation ___
46. Verdi masterpiece
47. Marvel superheroes (hyph.)
49. Mexican ___ dance

Crossword 39

ACROSS

1. "Message ___ Bottle" (2 wds.)
4. Dentist's degree (abbr.)
7. Brides' utterances (2 wds.)
11. Youth
12. Nobility title
14. Ripken, Sr. and Jr.
15. RMN's predecessor
16. German woman
17. Bad time for Caesar
18. Comic Johnson
20. ___ uniform
22. Part of CIA (abbr.)
24. Large pitcher
25. Like cotton candy
27. Limo passenger
28. "Bali ___"
31. Certain elected official (abbr.)
32. Axiom
34. Like an antique
35. Explosive letters
36. Moved swiftly
37. Alpaca's cousin
39. Young males
40. Historic periods
41. Merry tunes
43. Under the covers
45. Rowlands of film
46. Pocket for feta
48. Picks from a lineup
51. Envelope abbr.
52. Shortly
53. Hoop attachment
54. Like Mr. Clean
55. Compass letters
56. White-bearded antelope

DOWN

1. Sick
2. Seize suddenly
3. Next to
4. Skillful
5. Venture
6. Sp. woman's title
7. More aloof
8. June celebrants
9. Bullring cries
10. Snake's sound
13. Beethoven's first name
19. Seeded bread
21. Drive away
22. CEO's aide
23. Dancer Verdon

24. Dale or Linda
26. Fortunetelling card
28. Emulating a pack rat
29. ___ mater
30. Lupino and Tarbell
33. Facial locale (2 wds.)
38. Peggy or Brenda
39. Insipid
41. "___ smile be your umbrella" (2 wds.)
42. Worldwide (abbr.)
43. Like ___ of bricks (2 wds.)
44. Poison
45. Talk constantly
47. Country resort
49. Fox's lair
50. Trio after R

Crossword 40

ACROSS

1. Fan's cheer
4. Authors' submissions (abbr.)
7. '50s sound system (hyph.)
11. Wind direction (abbr.)
12. Between
14. Author Bagnold
15. Diamond woman
16. Actress Gershon
17. Conception
18. Make suitable
20. Where the sandman visits
22. Truth's opposite
23. Goren's game
27. James Galway's instrument
30. Juan's "hurrah"
31. Age
32. Highland miss
33. Mimic
34. U.S. citizen (abbr.)
35. Forelimb
36. Insider's advice
37. Circus buffoon
38. "Key Largo" actress

40. ___ Beta Kappa
41. Biol., e.g.
42. Insurance provider
45. Unappetizing food, slangily
48. Insect young
50. Apply frosting
52. Best-rated (2 wds.)
53. Canter, e.g.
54. School org.
55. Hired hoodlum
56. Numerals (abbr.)
57. Make a lap

DOWN

1. Aunt or uncle (abbr.)
2. Nepal's continent
3. Cradled
4. Noisy, mischievous bird
5. Strike, Bible-style
6. Serious wrong
7. Johanna Spyri book
8. Ky.'s neighbor
9. Word of disgust
10. Director Lupino
13. Play with, as a sideline
19. Heights (abbr.)
21. Sooner than, in poetry
24. Tape for a record exec
25. Swelled
26. Make cash

27. Excess fat
28. Zhivago's love
29. "Gomer Pyle, __"
30. Antonym (abbr.)
33. Not well
34. Dismounted
36. Doting attention (abbr.)
37. Treasure boxes
39. Quaking tree
40. Barbecue area
43. __ in the bud
44. "Hamlet" start (2 wds.)
45. Stage joke
46. Brit's bathroom
47. "Sail __ Ship of State!" (2 wds.)
49. John, in Aberdeen
51. Visit a diner

ACROSS

1. Holds
4. Inclined way
8. Cracked, as a door
12. Ga.'s neighbor
13. Flier to Tel Aviv (2 wds.)
14. Pen
15. Can metal
16. Heredity factor
17. Uprising in the streets
18. Gossip's Hopper
20. Brother of Cain
22. __ terrier
25. Barbecue residue
28. Prepare copy
30. Luncheonette
32. Make a selection
33. Sleuth, informally
34. Bravery
35. __ tree (cornered, 2 wds.)
36. German exclamation
37. A Guthrie
38. Organization (abbr.)
39. Places for earrings
41. Incline
43. Designer Cassini
45. Books of Moses
48. __ B'rith
50. College course (abbr.)
53. Stop __ dime (2 wds.)
54. Ernie's pal
55. Bestow
56. Middle (abbr.)
57. Surrender territory
58. Impersonator
59. Tool __

DOWN

1. "Hell __ no fury..."
2. "__ of the Mind" (2 wds.)
3. Advertising device (2 wds.)
4. Majestic
5. Pub brew
6. "The Invisible __"
7. Entreaty
8. Measures of land
9. Hit for Elvis (2 wds.)
10. Long __
11. Stop working (abbr.)
19. Investigator (abbr.)
21. Max of "The Beverly Hillbillies"
23. Wound memento

24. Lozenge brand
26. Omar of "House"
27. Comedian Laurel
28. List ender (2 wds.)
29. Art ___ (decorative art)
31. Simpleton
34. Bouquet holder
38. GI's address (abbr.)
40. Select bunch
42. Aquatic mammal
44. Infatuated, slangily
46. One against
47. Deer
48. English TV network
49. Society column "born"
51. Small taste
52. Wide street (abbr.)

Crossword 42

ACROSS

1. Cable choice for execs (abbr.)
5. Roof part
9. Unprincipled lout
12. Duncan toy (hyph.)
13. Marvel superheroes (hyph.)
14. "The Greatest" boxer
15. Soaking
17. Summer sign
18. Sot's offense (abbr.)
19. Disagree
21. Draw in, as a sponge
24. Late night weekend comedy show (abbr.)
25. Toothpaste topper
26. Not bright
28. Zealous
32. Boring
34. Sticky substance
36. Festival
37. Billiards shot
39. Iced __
41. Certain sweater sizes (abbr.)
42. Singer "King" Cole
44. Big-city teenagers' music culture (hyph.)
46. Mississippi city
49. House addition
50. Where Tel Aviv is (abbr.)
51. Cherished
56. Compass dir.
57. Discharge
58. End for hip or mob
59. Light knock
60. Guest rooms, often
61. The girl's

DOWN

1. Dancer Charisse
2. Neither's pal
3. Departer's shout
4. Tenant-owned apartment
5. Museum display
6. Friend (Fr.)
7. Peddles
8. Locomotive
9. Leg area
10. Skipper's direction
11. Couturier Christian
16. Word on a cottage cheese container
20. Pennant
21. Current indication
22. Theda of silent movies

23. Practice boxing
27. Gymnast's pad
29. Nasty cut
30. Red Muppet
31. Abrade
33. Rover's treat
35. Warms up last night's dinner
38. Fountain treat

40. Afflicts
43. Crooner Mel
45. First class
46. Balcony row
47. Middies' school (abbr.)
48. ___ school
52. One, in Bonn
53. Map abbr.
54. Bard's "always"
55. Surgeons, e.g. (abbr.)

Crossword 43

ACROSS

1. Apartment house, e.g. (abbr.)
5. Hoover's gp.
8. Extremely unfriendly
11. Famous Verdi opera
12. Love god
14. Bambi's mom, e.g.
15. __ St. Laurent
16. Pale color
17. "...__ mouse?" (2 wds.)
18. Gab
20. Indolent person
22. First father
24. Day-__ (fluorescent product)
25. Note taker, for short
26. Illness
30. Ref's kin
31. Texter's "wow!"
32. Minor-league level
33. Swimmer Williams and others
36. Hornets
38. Commercials
39. Smacks
40. Mario's brother in Nintendoland
43. Bouncer's station
45. Doctrine's suffix
46. __ the line (obeyed the rules)
48. Crimson Tide, familiarly
52. __ rally
53. Hardy
54. Southern constellation
55. Last-yr. students
56. "Treasure Island" inits.
57. Damsel

DOWN

1. Chesapeake __
2. Actress Tyler
3. 34th Pres.
4. Fuel holder (2 wds.)
5. Greek salad ingredient
6. Londoner, for short
7. Charged atom
8. Person on a pedestal
9. Apple center
10. Time division
13. Moonshine rig
19. Certain insurance plan (abbr.)
21. Champagne producer __ Pérignon
22. Cash dispensers (abbr.)
23. Lingerie or menswear, e.g. (abbr.)
24. Musician's job
25. Bring to court
26. Morning hrs.

27. Bidder's seat
28. Afternoon siestas
29. Professors' aides (abbr.)
31. Conjunctions
34. Crone
35. Mrs. Bunker
36. Question start
37. Car safety feature (2 wds.)

40. Kissing items
41. Computer operator
42. Mischievous sorts
43. Computer brand
44. Dedicative verses
47. Boating blade
49. Tycoon Onassis
50. Boss (abbr.)
51. Gmail alternative

Answers

PUZZLE 1

PUZZLE 2

PUZZLE 3

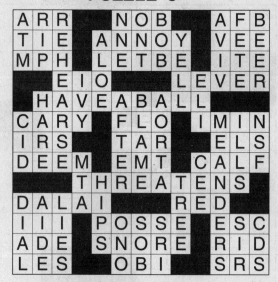

PUZZLE 4

PUZZLE 5

PUZZLE 6

L	I	D			B	A	N	S		B	F	F
A	S	I	F		A	T	O	P		L	I	T
B	R	E	R		C	L	V	I		A	D	D
		I	C	K			E	C	H	O		
	D	U	D	E		I	D	L	Y			
P	A	S	A	D	E	N	A		D	E	B	S
U	T	E		E	R	A	S	E		L	E	A
G	A	R	P		I	N	H	A	L	I	N	G
		E	L	E	E		C	E	E	S		
	L	E	G	O			G	H	I			
R	E	V		D	E	C	O		G	A	M	E
E	W	E		G	L	O	B		H	O	R	N
S	S	N		E	K	G	S		L	S	D	

PUZZLE 7

D	E	C		T	R	A	S	H		S	G	T
I	R	A		R	I	N	S	E		C	I	A
E	L	L		O	D	D	E	R		U	N	O
T	E	M	P	L	E	S		O	C	T		
		A	L	S		B	E	L	T	E	D	
	B	A	R	S		A	B	S	O	L	V	E
D	E	B	T		T	I	C		S	E	A	L
R	A	I	N	I	E	R		M	E	D	S	
E	U	G	E	N	E		S	I	T			
	A	R	F		C	E	N	S	U	R	E	
A	R	I		E	T	H	I	C		M	O	D
L	I	L		C	R	A	Z	E		P	I	G
A	M	S		T	I	N	E	S		S	L	Y

PUZZLE 8

B	C	D		C	O	W	L		A	C	E	D
I	R	E		A	R	I	A		H	O	L	E
N	E	T		B	E	S	T		A	C	M	E
G	E	E	N	A		P	C	S		K	O	S
	R	A	N	D		H	I	L	T			
C	O	M	R	A	D	E		B	E	A	D	S
H	A	I	R		S	A	C		A	I	D	A
I	F	N	O	T		T	A	C	K	L	E	D
	A	W	L	S		W	E	E	P			
C	A	T		C	H	E		A	D	A	G	E
A	L	I	T		I	D	E	S		R	O	B
S	L	O	B		F	I	N	E		T	A	B
S	I	N	S		T	E	S	S		Y	D	S

PUZZLE 9

F	O	A	L		H	E	M	P		W	E	B
C	O	P	A		A	L	A	I		R	Y	E
C	H	O	C	O	L	A	T	E	B	A	R	S
		E	V	E	L		C	A	P	E	S	
F	A	L	S	E			B	E	D			
A	S	I		N	C	A	A		G	A	Z	A
D	E	P	T		A	G	T		E	X	E	S
E	A	S	Y		B	O	S	C		E	R	A
		L	A	S			N	Y	L	O	N	
A	S	P	E	N		H	O	B	O			
S	H	O	R	T	C	I	R	C	U	I	T	S
T	A	T		E	O	N	S		N	O	W	S
O	D	S		D	O	D	O		G	N	A	T

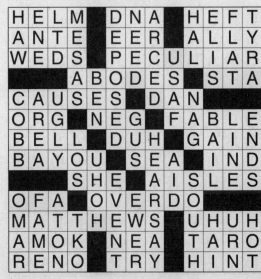

PUZZLE 10

M	P	S		R	O	Y		H	A	H	A
G	O	O		E	V	E	S		A	R	I	D
R	E	L	E	V	A	N	T		I	T	E	M
		T	U	L	S	A		R	E	D	S	
E	C	H	O	E	S		T	E	D			
G	L	E	N		E	U	R	O	P	E		
O	U	R		A	C	H	E	S		O	Y	S
	B	R	A	V	O	S		A	N	E	W	
		R	A	N		A	C	C	E	D	E	
W	E	B	B		V	A	P	O	R			
A	R	L	O		E	S	P	R	E	S	S	O
I	G	O	R		Y	A	L	E		I	R	K
F	O	G	S			P	E	R		P	O	S

PUZZLE 11

H	E	L	M		D	N	A		H	E	F	T
A	N	T	E		E	E	R		A	L	L	Y
W	E	D	S		P	E	C	U	L	I	A	R
			A	B	O	D	E	S		S	T	A
C	A	U	S	E	S		D	A	N			
O	R	G		N	E	G		F	A	B	L	E
B	E	L	L		D	U	H		G	A	I	N
B	A	Y	O	U		S	E	A		I	N	D
		S	H	E		A	I	S	L	E	S	
O	F	A		O	V	E	R	D	O			
M	A	T	T	H	E	W	S		U	H	U	H
A	M	O	K		N	E	A		T	A	R	O
R	E	N	O		T	R	Y		H	I	N	T

PUZZLE 12

T	H	E			B	I	D	S		O	L	D
R	E	T		C	A	N	O	E		O	E	R
A	R	A	B	I	A	N	N	I	G	H	T	S
		I	R	S		T	K	O				
	C	R	O	C				O	L	S	E	N
A	R	I		L	I	A	R		F	I	D	O
R	E	N		E	D	N	A	S		N	I	P
C	A	G	E		A	T	T	N		A	T	E
S	M	O	K	E			E	L	I	S		
		E	L	F		H	E	E				
N	E	W	S	M	A	G	A	Z	I	N	E	S
A	R	K		E	M	I	L	E		O	N	O
T	A	S		R	E	S	T		S	E	W	

PUZZLE 13

	B	A	I	T				A	B	C	
	B	E	W	A	R	E		F	R	E	E	D
I	L	L	E	G	A	L		I	R	E	N	E
D	U	I		O	C	E	A	N		T	S	E
L	E	E	R		E	N	G		K	L	U	M
E	S	S	E	S		A	T	O	N	E	S	
			P	A	C		S	K	I			
	A	G	A	T	H	A		S	T	A	G	E
A	B	L	Y		A	R	C		S	L	I	T
B	R	A		E	N	O	L	A		A	V	A
B	O	N	U	S		M	O	N	G	R	E	L
Y	A	C	H	T		A	U	T	U	M	N	
	D	E	S				D	I	M	S		

PUZZLE 14

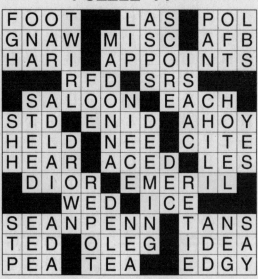

F	O	O	T		L	A	S		P	O	L
G	N	A	W		M	I	S	C		A	F	B
H	A	R	I		A	P	P	O	I	N	T	S
		R	F	D		S	R	S				
	S	A	L	O	O	N		E	A	C	H
S	T	D		E	N	I	D		A	H	O	Y
H	E	L	D		N	E	E		C	I	T	E
H	E	A	R		A	C	E	D		L	E	S
	D	I	O	R		E	M	E	R	I	L
		W	E	D		I	C	E			
S	E	A	N	P	E	N	N		T	A	N	S
T	E	D		O	L	E	G		I	D	E	A
P	E	A		T	E	A		E	D	G	Y

PUZZLE 15

H	A	G		W	E	E		M	A	S	S
O	R	E		A	W	O	L		A	L	U	M
O	I	L		M	I	N	I		N	I	P	S
P	A	T	T	I		A	L	O	E		
		E	D	A	M		I	F	N	O	T
H	E	W	S		B	I	A	S		A	R	E
A	L	E	S		E	S	P		E	T	T	A
T	E	L		A	L	T	S		D	E	S	K
H	E	L	M	S		Y	O	G	I		
	T	O	P	S			N	E	I	G	H
F	O	O	D		E	S	A	U		D	O	E
B	C	D	E		L	I	D	S		A	T	A
I	D	O	L		F	R	O		S	O	P

PUZZLE 16

B	E	E	F		G	E	E		A	T	O	P
A	L	V	A		E	A	T		L	I	A	M
G	M	A	N		N	R	A		E	E	K	S
		B	E	T		G	M	C				
L	O	P	E	S		P	E	A	S	A	N	T
O	P	A	L	S		R	R	S		S	A	O
G	R	I	T		T	E	E		A	S	I	N
I	A	N		I	R	E		A	B	O	V	E
C	H	E	C	K	I	N		F	A	C	E	D
		H	E	P		U	R	N				
B	O	O	R		P	E	G		D	E	N	S
A	U	D	I		E	E	L		O	W	N	S
D	I	E	S		D	R	Y		N	E	W	T

PUZZLE 17

C	H	A	D		B	F	F		G	O	A	D
H	A	V	E		A	O	L		A	L	L	Y
I	L	O	V	E	Y	O	U		P	I	T	A
T	O	W	E	L		L	I	D		V	O	N
		L	A	T		D	I	N	E		
E	N	R	O	L	L	S		G	O	O	F	S
B	E	E	P		C	S	A		T	I	D	Y
B	O	G	E	Y		S	C	H	O	L	A	R
	A	R	E	A		T	A	R			
B	A	R		A	D	E		R	I	O	D	E
A	L	D	A		M	A	C	K	E	R	E	L
M	A	E	S		I	R	A		T	E	A	S
A	I	D	A		T	N	T		Y	O	D	A

PUZZLE 18

```
CHAW  SIB   ACH
HORA  ALLS  BAA
IBMS  SKIT  CSI
COSTAS  MILDER
   ELI  PLO
WHISPER  TUBAS
ERS   RAM   AGE
TEMPO  HATSHOP
   AMI  COP
CALMER  BOOTHS
OHO  GIVE  NEAL
MAW  ASIT  GENA
ABS  HEH   EDDY
```

PUZZLE 19

```
ABE  ACDC   CPL
REL  MADAM  LIE
LAM  AMERICANA
ODORS   BLIP
   USB   LATE
ACRE  AIDE  RNA
MAE  ERROR  ADV
SSN  MARC  APSE
  HERB   SHA
  WOOS   EARTH
BRIMSTONE  AIM
EIN  SALAD  MNO
EGG   BENS  PAS
```

PUZZLE 20

```
IRV  OMITS  LIL
MOI  ROMEO  ETC
SER  ABANDONED
  GOT  SAM
EVIDENT  SARGE
PINS  ARF  REED
SCI   POE  LEG
OKAY  SOL  WISE
MINES  PLEASED
   LEE   ASH
BUMPERCAR  IND
MSS  KLEIN  NOR
WON  SENDS  GNU
```

PUZZLE 21

```
ALEC  RAF  GIGS
BOZO  ELL  ROME
BARNACLE  ANAT
ADAMS  ASHY
   ESC  HEEDED
CHANNEL  TRIPE
OOP   LOS   BIC
POPES  NABISCO
ATTEST  GUS
  YARD  FALSE
CAPO  OUTFIELD
AMER  TBA  AGOG
DATE  SSE  HOWE
```

PUZZLE 22

```
FCC  BASS  ATOM
AAH  ITEM  HARD
IVE  CIAO  EXES
REDEEM  LOADS
  DOPE  DUDE
SPANS  GER  DWI
OARS  SPR  DUOS
NYC  MPS  PACER
  HOPI  ALIT
  FEIGN  BESIDE
FEEL  AGUA  BOB
EASE  COST  LOB
BRER  HOES  EMS
```

PUZZLE 23

```
 CHA  POI  BACH
BOAR  APO  ELLA
CRUMBLED  AJAR
DEL  DENIM  ONT
  PARENTAL
MCCOY  DEARSIR
AFAR   CODY
CONGAME  SENSE
  BYPASSED
ACE  TITLE  AHA
NORA  THANKFUL
DARN  REV  ARRS
STAY  ERE  TOT
```

PUZZLE 24

```
OAT   AMMO  CAL
ALA  DIVAN  OYS
FINGERPAINTED
    LPS  MOE
  IGOT   NICKS
BRR  HAMS  LAIT
RAE  SPARE  RTE
ATTA  ERIQ  VET
DEALT    USES
    ORA  FAN
ROGUESGALLERY
AMP  NEEDS  UKE
PGA  DANE   ROT
```

PUZZLE 25

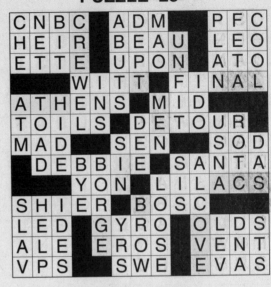

```
CNBC  ADM    PFC
HEIR  BEAU   LEO
ETTE  UPON   ATO
    WITT  FINAL
ATHENS  MID
TOILS  DETOUR
MAD    SEN    SOD
  DEBBIE  SANTA
    YON  LILACS
SHIER   BOSC
LED  GYRO   OLDS
ALE  EROS   VENT
VPS   SWE   EVAS
```

PUZZLE 26

```
HAG  TONIC   BAG
ERE  AVAIL   ERR
MEA  KATIE   ELI
ISRAEL   VENOM
   MRS   JEB
GENTS  HARBORS
TSE   BAM   EIO
OTTOMAN  ADROP
   WAR   SID
CALLS   TRENDS
ALE  HATED   ION
RIG  ELDER   PSI
REO  RASPY   SET
```

PUZZLE 27

```
ABA    PIC   DEMO
HONG   OFA   ESPN
MANOFLAMANCHA
ERASE  LEWS
   HEEL  LETGO
ADA   DOT   RAIL
BOB  SNOBS  RFD
COEN  PAN   STS
DREAM  IDAS
   CEDE  RAMBO
TECHNICALFOUL
ATNO  NED  ELLA
CANS  SSS   ELF
```

PUZZLE 28

```
PLEA  BUCK   MGM
HISS  AFRO   AUG
DESI  COOS   RMS
   AOK  CHIMP
  ANNALS  EVA
ARI  ROT  RELIC
TAGS  GAG  SAGA
ABHOR  SRA  DOM
   TRI  HOLDER
  POETS  WII
SAW  TOPS  ROMP
SNL  ESAU  GOAT
ASS  RAMP  EPPS
```

PUZZLE 29

```
CFO   NBC    FAT
HAUL  AAA   COLE
ARTE  MAR   ANDS
DESIRE  LINDAS
  IGOT  ORA
REDHEAD  ALBUM
ORE   GER    ASI
DARIN  NOTICED
   LEA  BUNK
ARMIES  BELFRY
BEAK  SHE  ELEE
BITE  EUR  TINT
YDS   SMS    POI
```

PUZZLE 30

C	S	I			C	O	P	A		E	G	O
Y	E	N	S		A	Y	E	S		D	I	N
D	A	N	E		A	L	P	S		I	G	O
			R	M	N		P	U	N	T	S	
G	R	A	V	E		D	E	M	I			
R	E	N	E	W		I	R	E	L	A	N	D
I	A	N		C	R	Y		M	O	O		
D	R	O	U	G	H	T		B	R	A	W	N
		S	L	A	Y		R	I	N	S	E	
	S	O	N	A	R		F	O	O			
E	L	M		R	A	G	E		T	A	B	S
L	O	A		E	D	N	A		S	P	E	W
S	P	R		D	E	U	T		R	T	E	

PUZZLE 31

D	O	T	E		B	A	B	A		U	M	A
A	L	E	X		I	B	E	T		R	A	W
B	E	E	P		R	E	N	O	U	N	C	E
			A	M	C		E	M	T			
H	A	N	N	A	H		F	I	E	N	D	S
E	R	O	D	E		B	I	C		O	R	T
A	R	T		M	A	T		M	A	A		
R	O	M		J	A	Y		K	H	A	K	I
S	W	E	D	E	S		G	L	I	D	E	R
		D	E	C		O	M	G				
P	A	S	T	R	A	M	I		H	A	R	P
I	R	R		E	R	I	N		E	K	E	S
P	C	S		D	A	N	G		R	A	P	T

PUZZLE 32

H	E	H			G	O	O	N		I	D	A
E	N	E		B	O	N	G	O		D	I	R
S	I	R		E	B	E	R	T		E	L	K
	D	O	L	L		A	E	R	I	A	L	
		P	I	E		S	E	C				
C	H	I	S	E	L	S		E	R	L	E	
P	E	R		F	L	O	O	R		K	E	N
A	P	E	S		B	O	O	B	O	O	S	
		A	C	T		H	U	E				
	D	R	P	H	I	L		G	E	E	S	
V	I	E		A	L	I	N	E		T	K	O
A	S	A		F	E	A	R	S		A	I	L
N	H	L		E	R	M	A		L	T	D	

PUZZLE 33

C	L	A	Y		C	H	E	W		C	A	D
B	O	N	E		A	R	E	A		H	U	R
S	U	N	S	C	R	E	E	N		A	T	E
			E	E	L		T	H	R	O	W	
C	E	A	S	E		F	R	A	U			
A	L	S		H	O	O	D	L	U	M	S	
F	E	T	A		A	R	M		A	S	A	P
E	M	I	N	E	N	C	E		E	K	E	
		E	L	K	E		E	R	R	E	D	
S	C	O	W	L		H	I	E				
A	O	L		E	D	G	I	N	G	O	U	T
I	T	E		R	O	A	R		I	F	S	O
D	E	G		Y	A	L	E		S	T	A	T

PUZZLE 34

A	F	B		A	B	B	A		S	A	N
F	L	O		S	U	I	T	E		P	I	N
L	U	N	C	H	R	O	O	M		A	D	E
		A	L	P		E	F	G				
	W	I	S	E		D	I	N	A	H	S	
L	A	N	K	Y		A	N	D	R	E	W	S
A	R	F		H	R	S		T	A	R		
T	O	O	L	K	I	T		D	I	T	T	O
	F	R	O	N	T	S		E	L	I	S	
	M	O	I		A	L	L					
C	H	A		F	I	R	S	T	S	T	E	P
D	A	N		E	V	I	T	A		A	G	O
S	I	T		E	N	O	S		P	G	S	

PUZZLE 35

B	B	C		B	L	O	A	T		S	A	G
R	O	O		A	C	U	R	A		H	I	P
A	N	D		I	D	I	O	T		O	D	S
		D	E	A	L		D	E	L	V	E	
		L	I	E	N		R	A	E			
S	H	U	F	F	L	E	S		B	L	D	G
K	A	N		F	L	A	I	R		E	W	E
I	M	I	N		S	P	L	E	N	D	I	D
		C	O	S		S	O	L	E			
	D	O	N	N	A		I	G	E	T		
A	R	R		O	F	T	E	N		T	E	L
T	I	N		R	A	I	S	E		T	E	A
M	P	S		T	R	E	E	S		A	M	P

PUZZLE 36

	T	H	R	O	B		B	B	S	
S	E	A	A	I	R		R	O	G	E	R
M	A	N	G	L	E		O	B	T	A	I	N
O	C	D			S	A	R	A	S		S	T	A
G	U	L	F		K	I	D		L	E	A	P
	P	E	L	T	E	D		D	I	R	S	
		I	S	R		S	A	L				
	D	A	R	K		C	A	S	A	B	A	
P	E	S	T		H	A	D		C	A	G	E
A	F	T		G	O	L	D	A		T	R	A
C	O	O	G	A	N		E	M	O	T	E	R
	G	R	O	P	E		N	O	B	L	E	S
		D	E	S		S	K	I	E	D		

PUZZLE 37

M	O	B		D	W	E	L	T		A	D	O
A	H	A		R	O	D	E	O		R	E	M
J	O	H	N	A	L	D	E	N		G	E	E
			I	F	F	Y		T	H	O	R	N
G	I	A	N	T			C	O	O			
A	N	S		E	A	S	E		E	D	I	E
L	O	T		E	X	T	O	L		A	T	L
A	N	A	T		E	L	S	E		D	E	M
			O	K	S			S	H	A	M	S
F	E	L	O	N		B	A	S	S			
R	C	A		O	P	E	R	E	T	T	A	S
O	H	S		C	H	A	I	N		H	M	O
G	O	T		K	I	N	D	S		Y	A	Y

PUZZLE 38

A	H	S			H	A	S		S	K	I	D
L	E	T		F	E	D	S		H	I	D	E
M	M	E		E	L	L	E		A	L	L	A
A	S	P		A	M	I		L	L	O	Y	D
		O	R	R		B	E	A	T			
A	O	N	E		E	S	P	Y		T	A	D
F	R	I	N	G	E		I	S	L	A	N	D
R	S	T		A	L	E	C		B	L	T	S
			D	I	S	C		A	S	K		
L	A	T	I	N		L	A	S		S	A	X
A	S	A	N		H	A	R	I		H	I	M
W	E	R	E		A	I	M	S		O	D	E
N	A	P	S		T	R	Y		W	A	N	

PUZZLE 39

I	N	A		D	D	S		I	D	O	S	
L	A	D		E	A	R	L		C	A	L	S
L	B	J		F	R	A	U		I	D	E	S
		A	R	T	E		D	R	E	S	S	
A	G	C	Y		E	W	E	R				
S	W	E	E	T		V	I	P		H	A	I
S	E	N		A	D	A	G	E		O	L	D
T	N	T		R	A	N		L	L	A	M	A
			B	O	Y	S			E	R	A	S
	L	I	L	T	S		A	B	E	D		
G	E	N	A		P	I	T	A		I	D	S
A	T	T	N		A	N	O	N		N	E	T
B	A	L	D			N	N	E		G	N	U

PUZZLE 40

R	A	H		M	S	S		H	I	F	I	
E	S	E		A	M	I	D		E	N	I	D
L	I	L		G	I	N	A		I	D	E	A
	A	D	A	P	T		B	E	D			
		L	I	E		B	R	I	D	G	E	
F	L	U	T	E		O	L	E		E	R	A
L	A	S	S		A	P	E		A	M	E	R
A	R	M		T	I	P		C	L	O	W	N
B	A	C	A	L	L		P	H	I			
			S	C	I		A	E	T	N	A	
G	L	O	P		N	I	T	S		I	C	E
A	O	N	E		G	A	I	T		P	T	A
G	O	O	N		N	O	S		S	I	T	

PUZZLE 41

H	A	S		R	A	M	P		A	J	A	R
A	L	A		E	L	A	L		C	A	G	E
T	I	N		G	E	N	E		R	I	O	T
H	E	D	D	A			A	B	E	L		
	W	E	L	S	H		A	S	H	E	S	
E	D	I	T		C	A	F	E		O	P	T
T	E	C		V	A	L	O	R		U	P	A
A	C	H		A	R	L	O		A	S	S	N
L	O	B	E	S		S	L	O	P	E		
		O	L	E	G			T	O	R	A	H
B	N	A	I		A	N	A	T		O	N	A
B	E	R	T		G	I	V	E		C	T	R
C	E	D	E		A	P	E	R		K	I	T

PUZZLE 42

C	N	B	C	■	E	A	V	E	■	C	A	D
Y	O	Y	O	■	X	M	E	N	■	A	L	I
D	R	E	N	C	H	I	N	G	■	L	E	O
■	■	■	D	U	I	■	D	I	F	F	E	R
A	B	S	O	R	B	■	S	N	L	■	■	■
C	A	P	■	D	I	M	■	E	A	G	E	R
D	R	A	B	■	T	A	R	■	G	A	L	A
C	A	R	O	M	■	T	E	A	■	S	M	S
■	■	N	A	T	■	H	I	P	H	O	P	■
T	U	P	E	L	O	■	E	L	L	■	■	■
I	S	R	■	T	R	E	A	S	U	R	E	D
E	N	E	■	E	M	I	T	■	S	T	E	R
R	A	P	■	D	E	N	S	■	H	E	R	S

PUZZLE 43

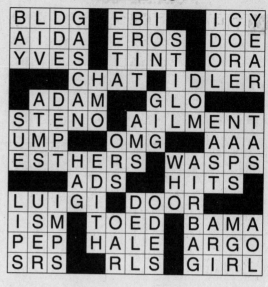

B	L	D	G	■	F	B	I	■	■	I	C	Y
A	I	D	A	■	E	R	O	S	■	D	O	E
Y	V	E	S	■	T	I	N	T	■	O	R	A
■	■	C	H	A	T	■	I	D	L	E	R	■
■	A	D	A	M	■	G	L	O	■	■	■	■
S	T	E	N	O	■	A	I	L	M	E	N	T
U	M	P	■	O	M	G	■	■	A	A	A	■
E	S	T	H	E	R	S	■	W	A	S	P	S
■	■	A	D	S	■	■	H	I	T	S	■	■
L	U	I	G	I	■	D	O	O	R	■	■	■
I	S	M	■	T	O	E	D	■	B	A	M	A
P	E	P	■	H	A	L	E	■	A	R	G	O
S	R	S	■	R	L	S	■	G	I	R	L	■